Practice in the Basic Skills

Contents

Published by Collins Educational
An imprint of HarperCollins*Publishers* Ltd
77-85 Fulham Palace Road
London W6 8JB

www.CollinsEducation.com
On-line support for schools and colleges

© Derek Newton and David Smith 2003
First published 1978
This edition published 2003
Reprinted 10 9 8 7 6

ISBN-13 978-0-00-7177189

The authors assert the moral right to be identified as the authors of this work.

British Library Cataloguing in Publication Data
A catalogue record for this book is available from the British Library.

Illustrated by A Rodger

Printed by Gopsons Papers Ltd., India

Name these things ²

These start with **a**	These start with **b**	These start with **c**
1 a _ _ _	**6** b _ _	**11** c _ _
2 a _ _ _	**7** b _ _	**12** c _ _
3 a _ _ _ _	**8** b _ _	**13** c _ _
4 a _ _ _ _ _ _	**9** b _ _ _	**14** c _ _
5 a _ _ _ _ _	**10** b _ _	**15** c _ _ _ _

---

bee   apple   cap   bat   anchor   car   ball   ant   camel
cat   bed   acrobat   cup   axe   bus

Name these things

1. d _ _

2. d _ _ _

3. d _ _ _

4. e _ _

5. e _ _ _ _ _ _ _

6. f _ _

7. f _ _ _

8. f _ _ _

9. g _ _ _

10. g _ _ _ _ _

11. h _ _

12. h _ _

13. h _ _ _

14. h _ _ _ _ _

15. h _ _ _ _ _

girl   hat   garden   dog   egg   hammer   fox   horse
elephant   fire   duck   hand   desk   hen   fish

Name these things

1 i _ _ _ _ _	**6** k _ _ _	**11** m _ _ _
2 j _ _ _ _	**7** l _ _ _	**12** m _ _
3 j _ _	**8** l _ _ _ _	**13** m _ _ _
4 k _ _	**9** l _ _ _ _ _	**14** n _ _ _
5 k _ _ _	**10** l _ _ _	**15** n _ _ _

mat   jam   nest   ladder   kite   insect   lamb   moon
lion   jelly   key   lemon   nose   king   milk

Name these things

1 o _ _ _ _ _	6 qu _ _ _	11 s _ _
2 o _ _ _ _ _ _	7 r _ _	12 s _ _
3 p _ _	8 r _ _ _ _	13 t _ _
4 p _ _	9 r _ _ _ _	14 t _ _ _
5 p _ _ _	10 r _ _ _	15 t _ _ _

rat   pipe   queen   tree   orange   pin   robin   sun
tent   pig   octopus   roof   tap   saw   ruler

Name these things

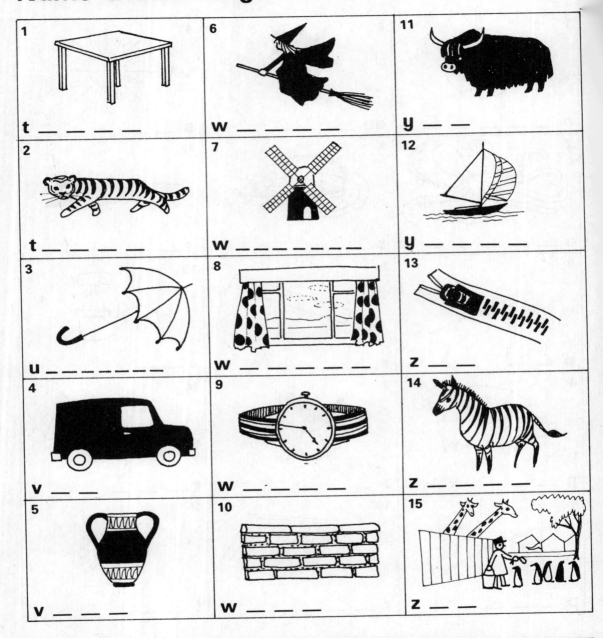

1. t _ _ _ _

2. t _ _ _ _

3. u _ _ _ _ _ _ _ _

4. v _ _ _

5. v _ _ _

6. w _ _ _ _

7. w _ _ _ _ _ _ _

8. w _ _ _ _ _ _

9. w _ _ _ _

10. w _ _ _

11. y _ _

12. y _ _ _ _

13. z _ _

14. z _ _ _ _

15. z _ _

watch   zoo   yak   tiger   witch   zip   table   vase
wall   yacht   van   window   umbrella   zebra   windmill

First sounds

Write each answer as a word.

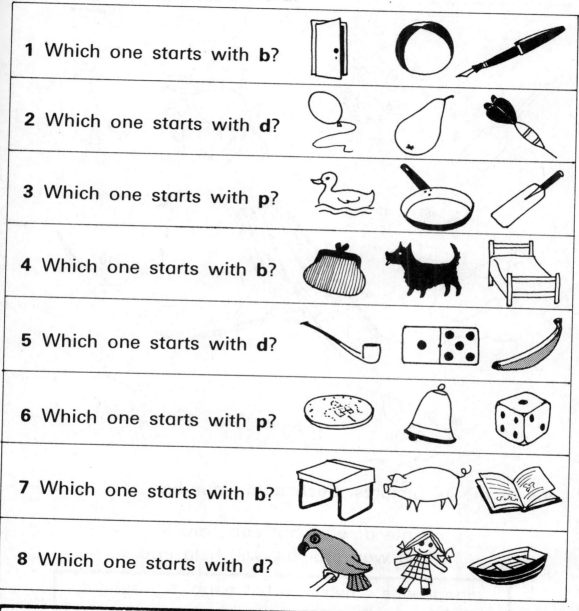

1 Which one starts with **b**?

2 Which one starts with **d**?

3 Which one starts with **p**?

4 Which one starts with **b**?

5 Which one starts with **d**?

6 Which one starts with **p**?

7 Which one starts with **b**?

8 Which one starts with **d**?

book   pan   doll   ball   domino   penny   dart   bed

Seen at the seaside

Look at the 14 pictures. Each has a number.

Write down what each one is.
The words below will help you.

sandcastle	fish	crab	pebbles	seagull
rocks	yacht	net	speedboat	pier
seaweed	spade	deckchair	cliffs	

Sorting animals

Write the correct animal's name for each picture.

1 camel   **2** _____   **3** _____   **4 and so on.**

These animal names will help you.

| rabbit leopard dog pig sheep cow |
| hamster camel giraffe gorilla hen cat |

Now draw three boxes and label them.
Write the names of the animals in the correct boxes.

home	**farm**	**zoo**
		camel

Watch us

1 Watch Susan _____.

2 Watch Andrew _____.

3 Watch Peter _____.

4 Watch Jane _____.

5 Watch Carol _____.

6 Watch Tom _____.

jump   run   climb   swim   skip   slide

More than one (1)

Look at these pictures.

Finish these sentences.

1 There are three _____.

2 There are nine _____.

3 There are two _____.

4 There are five _____.

5 There are four _____.

6 There are seven _____.

7 There are eight _____.

8 There are six _____.

| star | ball | car | house | bird | book | ladder | flower |

At home

Look at the picture. 14 things have a number.
  Write down what each one is.
  The words below will help you.

1 chair   **2** _____   **3** _____   **4** and so on.

television   settee   window   vase   lamp
chair   curtains   door   radio   carpet
fire   picture   table   books

Young animals

Now do these.
The words below will help you.

	Mother →	baby
1	cat →	_ _ _ _ _ _
2	dog →	_ _ _ _ _
3	hen →	_ _ _ _ _ _ _
4	duck →	_ _ _ _ _ _ _ _
5	cow →	_ _ _ _
6	horse →	_ _ _ _
7	sheep →	_ _ _ _
8	pig →	_ _ _ _ _ _

kitten   lamb   piglet   puppy
duckling   foal   calf   chicken

Ball play

1
Paul can ____ the ball.

2
Carol can ____ the ball.

3
Susan can ____ the ball.

4
Peter can ____ the ball.

5
Andrew can ____ the ball.

6
Jane can ____ the ball.

| throw | catch | kick | head | roll | bounce |

Crosswords

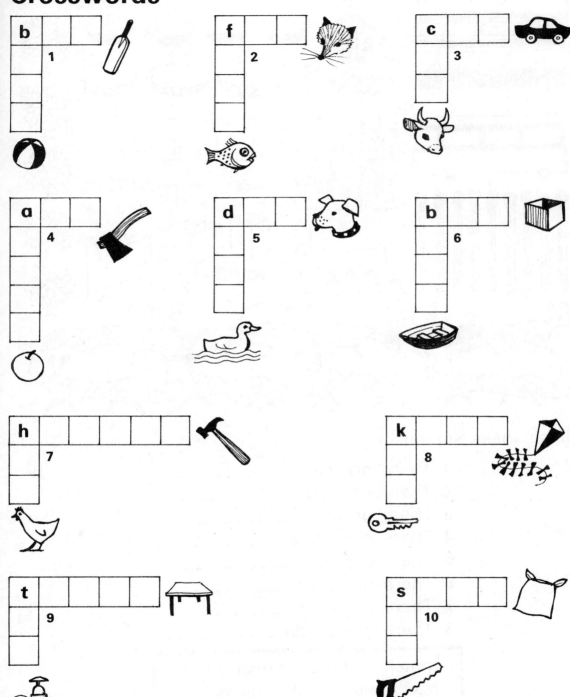

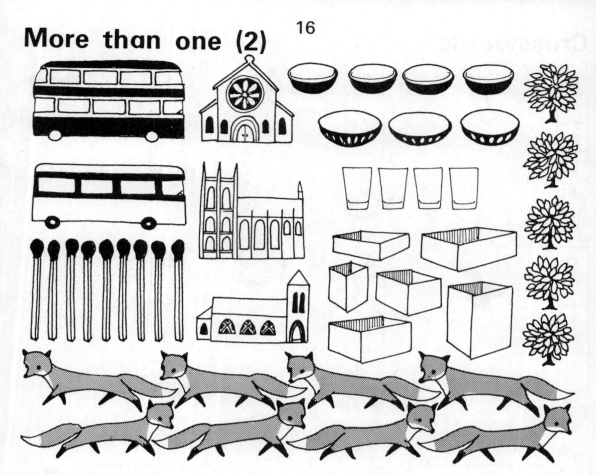

Finish these sentences.

1 There are nine _____.

2 There are four _____.

3 There are six _____.

4 There are three _____.

5 There are five _____.

6 There are eight _____.

7 There are two _____.

8 There are seven _____.

match	church	dish	box
fox	bus	bush	glass

At school

Look at the picture. 14 things have a number.

    Write down what each one is.
The words below will help you.

1 balance   2 _____   and so on.

> easel sand-tray books oven scissors
> aquarium pencils milk sink brushes
> ruler work-tray paints balance

Animal homes

Where do these animals live?

The words below will help you.

1 A badger → **s e t t**

2 A dog → _ _ _ _ _ _

3 A bee → _ _ _ _

4 A horse → _ _ _ _ _ _

5 A rabbit → _ _ _ _ _ _

6 A pig → _ _ _

7 A fox → _ _ _

8 A bird → _ _ _ _

| nest | hive | sty | burrow | den | stable | sett | kennel |

They are busy

1 Jane likes to _____.

2 Andrew likes to _____.

3 Paul likes to _____.

4 Carol likes to _____.

5 Susan likes to _____.

6 Peter likes to _____.

| sing | paint | bake | dig | sew | fish |

a in the middle

Fill in the right word.
The pictures and words will help you.
1 We boil eggs in a _____.
2 I like _____ on my bread.
3 I wear a _____ on my head.
4 I wipe my feet on a _____.
5 Mum carries shopping in a _____.

| bag | cap | pan | jam | mat |

e in the middle

10

Fill in the right word.
The pictures and words will help you.
1 The _____ is a useful bird.
2 I sleep in a _____.
3 Five and five are _____.
4 I have a right and a left _____.
5 I write with a _____.

| pen | ten | leg | bed | hen |

i in the middle

Fill in the right word.
   The pictures and words will help you.
   1 A part of your mouth. _____
   2 We put litter in a _____.
   3 A _____ has a very sharp point.
   4 Baked beans come in a _____.
   5 We get pork and bacon from a _____.

> pig   pin   lip   bin   tin

o in the middle

  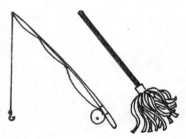

Fill in the right word.
   The pictures and words will help you.
   1 A baby sleeps in a _____.
   2 Mum cleans the floor with a _____.
   3 A thick piece of tree. _____
   4 A _____ is a pet.
   5 I catch fish with a _____.

> rod   log   cot   dog   mop

u in the middle

Fill in the right word.
The pictures and words will help you.

1 A small carpet. _____
2 A farm animal. _____
3 The _____ shines in the sky.
4 I drink out of a _____.
5 A _____ carries people.

> bus   sun   rug   bull   mug

Mixed bag

Fill in the right word.
The pictures and words will help you.

1 A pet. _____
2 See the squirrel eat a _____.
3 Peas grow in a _____.
4 A spider makes a _____.
5 You put rubbish into a _____.

> web   nut   cat   bin   pod

In the park

Look carefully at the picture.
  Finish these sentences.

1 _____ is coming down the slide.
2 There are _____ ducks in the pond.
3 _____ is playing with his boat.
4 _____ is feeding the swan.
5 _____ kicks the ball to _____.
6 _____ is skipping.
7 _____ and _____ are on the swings.
8 There are _____ trees in the park.
9 _____ and _____ are on the seesaw.
10 There are _____ children in the park.

Word puzzles (1)

Write the words correctly.

Here is an example **gba → bag**

These words will help you.

bat	car	mug	bee	web	sun	bed
bus	boy	cat	dog	cow	saw	tap

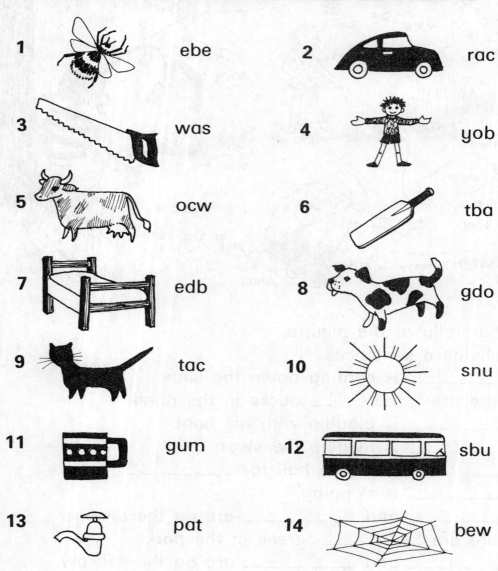

1 ebe

2 rac

3 was

4 yob

5 ocw

6 tba

7 edb

8 gdo

9 tac

10 snu

11 gum

12 sbu

13 pat

14 bew

Animal sounds

Find the correct sounds.
The words below will help you.

1 A cat _ _ _ _ _.
2 A dog _ _ _ _ _.
3 A pig _ _ _ _ _ _.
4 A duck _ _ _ _ _ _.
5 A lion _ _ _ _ _.
6 A lamb _ _ _ _ _ _.
7 A monkey _ _ _ _ _ _ _ _.
8 An owl _ _ _ _ _.

purrs	roars	chatters	bleats
hoots	barks	quacks	grunts

oo in the middle

1 b _ _ _ _

2 h _ _ _ _

3 b _ _ _ _

4 p _ _ _ _

5 g _ _ _ _

6 r _ _ _ _

7 r _ _ _ _

8 r _ _ _ _

9 s _ _ _ _ _

10 b _ _ _ _ _

11 h _ _ _ _

12 b _ _ _ _ _

goose   stool   root   book   boot   broom
rook   pool   brook   roof   hoop   hook

Rhymes (1)

Which word has the same sound as the word in bold type?

Write your answers like this:

1 man   **can**

2 cap   _____ and so on.

1 man	may	mat	can	run
2 cap	car	tap	lot	cat
3 mat	cat	bed	man	may
4 bed	boy	fin	bad	red
5 pen	leg	log	ten	pig
6 net	pet	not	put	mat
7 nib	rid	nip	bin	rib
8 lid	lit	kid	dim	lip
9 pig	wig	tip	pot	pad
10 lip	kit	hid	dip	tin
11 pin	bit	fin	pip	tip
12 rod	hop	cot	fog	pod
13 log	mop	dog	pot	rob
14 mop	dot	nod	top	cot
15 cot	dot	cod	dog	top
16 bud	bus	cub	sum	mud
17 rug	mug	gum	tub	rub
18 sun	nut	tug	gun	bud
19 cup	bun	pup	cub	bus
20 hut	hub	fun	mum	nut

Choose the right word

Look at each picture carefully.
  Write out the correct word for the picture like this:
1 plaice   **2** _____, and so on.

1 plaice plate place	**2** aunt and ant	**3** boy buoy buy
4 beer bear bare	**5** beech beach bench	**6** quay key kerb
7 pale pail paid	**8** sea say see	**9** rose rows nose
10 flour floor flower	**11** wood would world	**12** pair pear pare

Double letters

Many words have double letters, like apple and book.
  The pictures will help you.
  Write the answers like this:

1 apple   **2** _____, and so on.

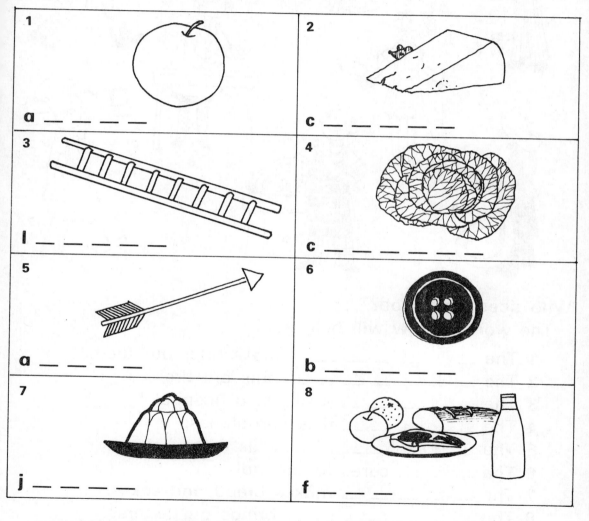

1 a _ _ _ _ _

2 c _ _ _ _ _

3 l _ _ _ _ _ _

4 c _ _ _ _ _ _

5 a _ _ _ _ _

6 b _ _ _ _ _ _

7 j _ _ _ _

8 f _ _ _ _

| ladder | button | jelly | cheese |
| apple | food | cabbage | arrow |

People at work

Who does which job?
The words below will help you.

1 The _ _ _ _ _ _ _ looks after our teeth.
2 The _ _ _ _ _ _ _ puts out fires.
3 The _ _ _ _ _ works in a hospital.
4 The _ _ _ _ _ _ flies aeroplanes.
5 The _ _ _ _ _ _ _ sells meat.
6 The _ _ _ cares for animals.
7 The _ _ _ _ _ makes bread and cakes.
8 The _ _ _ _ _ _ _ brings our letters.

dentist   pilot   butcher   vet
baker   postman   nurse   fireman

Word puzzles (2)

Write the words correctly.
Here is an example   **olin → lion**
These words will help you.

> moon king book nail boat tree bird
> leaf duck fish girl loaf foot goat

1 abot

2 drib

3 shif

4 lirg

5 aefl

6 onom

7 otof

8 olaf

9 kobo

10 rete

11 tgao

12 cudk

13 lian

14 ignk

Crosswords

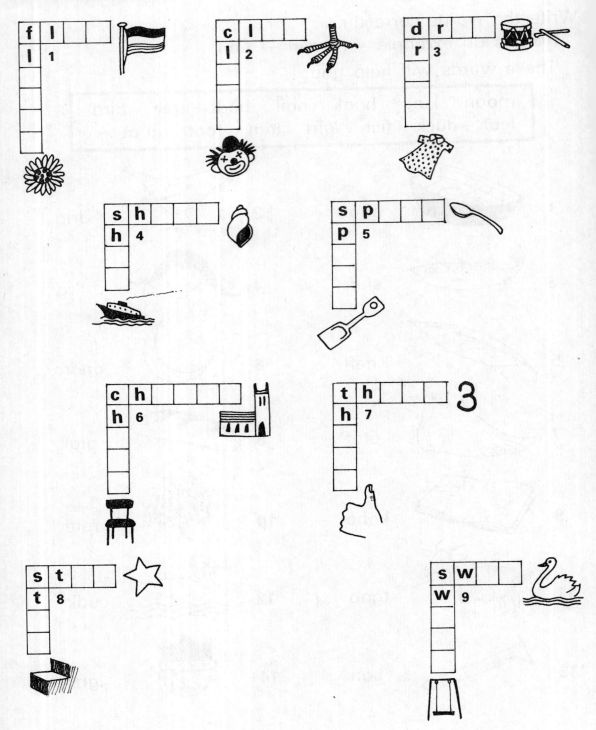

Completing sentences

A These sentences have been divided, but the halves are not in the right order.

Write out the correct sentences.

1 The gorilla . . . . . .   swam away.

2 Birds . . . .   has a roof.

3 The fish . . . . . .   scored a goal.

4 The airliner . . . . . .   was in the zoo.

5 Mark . . . . . .   landed at the airport.

6 A house . . . . . .   have feathers.

B A word has been left out of these sentences.

Choose the right word from the brackets to complete the sentences.

The first one has been done for you.

1 Tom **shuts** the door.   (shuts, bends, sleeps)

2 The dog _____ his tail.   (sits, wags, runs)

3 The farmer _____ the cow.   (runs, looks, milks)

4 Jane _____ into the mirror.   (lifts, looks, digs)

5 The postman _____ the letters.   (builds, feeds, brings)

6 Dad _____ his motor car.   (drives, bakes, writes)

7 Sue _____ her bicycle.   (reads, rides, barks)

8 Mum _____ the clothes.   (paints, writes, washes)

9 Mark always _____ his teeth every day.   (writes, brushes, sits)

10 The baby _____ in the pram.   (runs, sleeps, writes)

What are they?

Fill in the correct word.
These words will help you.

numbers	months	tools	fruits	boys
flowers	letters	birds	seasons	fish

1 Apple and orange are _____.
2 Winter and summer are _____.
3 Robin and thrush are _____.
4 Six and nine are _____.
5 Cod and herring are _____.
6 January and July are _____.
7 D and F are _____.
8 Hammer and saw are _____.
9 Paul and Mark are _____.
10 Daisy and buttercup are _____.

Words that begin with ch

Choose the right word.
The words below will help you.

1 Fish and _____.
2 I use _____ to write on the blackboard.
3 People pray to God in _____.
4 A young girl or boy. _____
5 A large, strong box. _____
6 I sit on a _____.

| chest   church   chair   chips   chalk   child |

Words that end with ch

1 A _____ helps you to see in the dark.
2 We play football on a _____.
3 _____ is the third month of the year.
4 I tell the time with a _____.
5 A _____ has a broomstick.
6 You can use a _____ to start fire.

| pitch   witch   watch   March   torch   match |

Colours

| brown | silver | blue | white | green | red | yellow | black |

Complete these sentences. Choose the correct colour from the list above.

1 A buttercup is _____.
2 Snow is _____.
3 Grass is _____.
4 Chocolate is _____.
5 Coal is _____.
6 The moon is _____.
7 A pillar box is _____.
8 The sky is _____.

Opposites

| weak | empty | straight | new | fast |
| quiet | dirty | hard | early | wet |

Write the opposite of the word in bold type, choosing from the list above.

1 My book is **old**, but yours is _____.
2 Ian was **late** for school, but Clare was _____.
3 David is a **slow** worker, but Paul is _____.
4 The elephant is **strong**, but the mouse is _____.
5 My toffee is **soft**, but yours is _____.
6 Your hands are **dry**, but mine are _____.
7 This room is _____, but that room is **noisy**.
8 I have a **full** bottle of pop, but yours is _____.
9 The corridor is _____, but the hall is **clean**.
10 That line is **bent**, while that one is _____.

Rhymes (2)

Which word has the same sound as the word in bold type?
Write your answers like this:

1 fly   cry   2 bread _____, and so on.

1 fly	cry	two	may	flop
2 bread	bead	bear	head	bored
3 rain	rail	train	ran	wait
4 tray	toy	try	door	day
5 sail	nail	fall	soil	foil
6 neat	near	more	meat	need
7 soon	sort	moon	soot	sun
8 grow	blue	group	groan	blow
9 joy	toy	top	jam	bow
10 cow	cap	cut	now	grow
11 nose	must	rose	news	noise
12 glue	glad	blow	glum	blue
13 late	lame	hate	lane	lake
14 gold	held	gulp	grab	sold
15 son	sun	saw	burn	some
16 bare	bore	fair	bead	bow
17 stain	stair	stone	lane	blame
18 made	maid	male	mare	make
19 word	board	ward	bird	work
20 their	thin	there	them	those

is or are

Complete the sentences using **is** or **are**.
1 The dog _____ in the field.
2 The dogs _____ in the field.
3 The cup _____ on the table.
4 Janet _____ my sister.
5 The lemons _____ sour.
6 _____ this your coat?
7 Tim and David _____ over there.
8 There _____ my house.
9 _____ these your books?
10 Kittens _____ playful.

was or were

Complete the sentences using **was** or **were**.
1 The bus _____ late.
2 The bread _____ stale.
3 The apples _____ sweet.
4 Linda _____ skipping.
5 The girls _____ in the park.
6 _____ your book exciting?
7 Susan and Heather _____ early for school.
8 The cows _____ in the field.
9 The buses _____ late.
10 _____ you at the football match?

Who's who?

Fill in the correct word.

| pilot dentist fireman nurse |
| farmer miner fisherman vet |

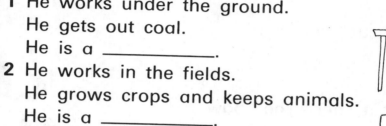

1 He works under the ground.
He gets out coal.
He is a _____.

2 He works in the fields.
He grows crops and keeps animals.
He is a _____.

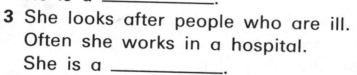

3 She looks after people who are ill.
Often she works in a hospital.
She is a _____.

4 He cares for sick animals.
He is a _____.

5 He works on a boat.
He uses a net.
He is a _____.

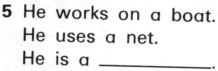
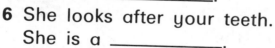

6 She looks after your teeth.
She is a _____.

7 He is often in the air.
He travels quickly.
He is a _____.

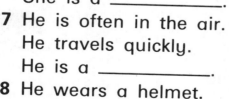

8 He wears a helmet.
He is brave.
He is a _____.

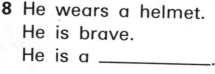

Jumbled sentences

Arrange the following words to make sentences.

1 goal Mark a scored

2 finger cut Ian his

3 licks cat her The paw

4 pond Kate the into fell

5 the Dad lawn cuts

6 lit Heather bonfire the

7 a Andrew letter posted

8 gate The over horse the jumped

a and an

Write **a** or **an** before each of the following words.

1 ____ cup   2 ____ apple

3 ____ donkey   4 ____ leg

5 ____ orange   6 ____ ear

7 ____ nose   8 ____ horse

9 ____ arm   10 ____ girl

11 ____ umbrella   12 ____ owl

13 ____ desk   14 ____ hen

15 ____ island

Complete the sentences using **a** or **an**.

1 Mum gave me ____ orange.

2 A mouse is smaller than ____ elephant.

3 Kim bought ____ ice cream.

4 Paul wore ____ anorak.

5 Heather found ____ umbrella.

6 David gave Peter ____ football.

7 Dad sat in ____ armchair and read ____ book.

8 A bird built ____ nest in ____ oak tree.

9 Sam ate ____ apple and ____ pear.

10 Sometimes ____ Eskimo lives in ____ igloo.

By the seaside

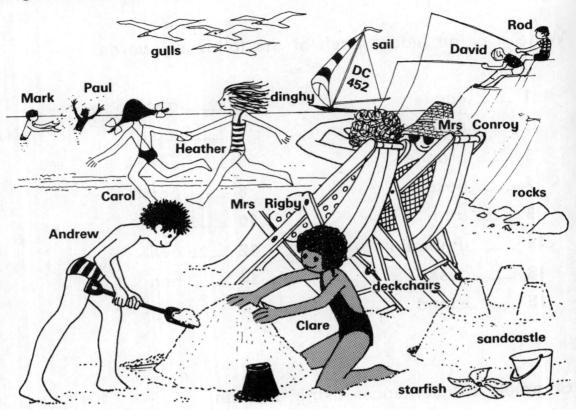

Look carefully at the picture.
Finish these sentences.

1 There are _____ gulls flying in the sky.

2 _____ and _____ are fishing from the rocks.

3 _____ and _____ are splashing in the sea.

4 _____ and _____ are running to the sea.

5 _____ and _____ are making a sandcastle.

6 A _____ is near the sandcastle.

7 _____ and _____ are in the deckchairs.

8 I can read _____ on the sail of the dinghy.

Choosing words

A Pick out six foods.

eggs	matches	bread	pebbles
sticks	coal	string	apples
pans	bacon	books	bottles
onions	spoons	cakes	watches

B Pick out six things we see on a farm.

fields	lions	plough	barn
soldiers	cows	parrots	train
hens	planes	ship	elephant
igloos	shop	tractor	rocket

C Pick out six things we wear.

boots	books	stairs	jackets
tools	shoes	jeans	bricks
shirts	cups	boxes	rugs
mirrors	pencils	fields	skirts

D Pick out six things that travel on roads.

buses	ships	castles	bicycles
planes	motorbikes	books	houses
helicopters	schools	forests	taxis
lorries	yachts	cars	boats

Find the best word

Complete the following sentences by choosing the best word from the list.

A

cruel	brave	blind	heavy	busy

1 The _____ man kicked the puppy.
2 A _____ man cannot see.
3 The _____ fireman rescued the lady from the fire.
4 Tom found the box too _____ to lift.
5 Christmas is a _____ time in the shops.

B

sharp	sour	steep	loud	sweet

1 The mountain was too _____ to climb.
2 Sugar is _____.
3 Bill cut his finger on a _____ knife.
4 The firework made a _____ noise.
5 The lemon was _____.

C

unhappy	fierce	dirty	difficult	bright

1 The wildcat is a _____ animal.
2 Sally cried because she was _____.
3 Michael could not see because the sun was _____.
4 John was _____ after he fell in the mud.
5 The puzzle was too _____ for David to finish.

The best word

Complete the following sentences by choosing the best word from the list.

A

banged   blew   ate   swam   asked

1 The rabbit _____ two carrots.
2 The fish _____ under the weeds.
3 Gary _____ his drum.
4 Mary _____ me to go for a walk.
5 The strong wind _____ down the tree.

B

chased   drank   crawled   flew   marched

1 The soldiers _____ along the road.
2 Joan was so thirsty she _____ two bottles of pop.
3 The aeroplane _____ from London to Paris.
4 The dog _____ the cat out of the garden.
5 Jenny _____ under the hedge for the ball.

C

whispered   baked   climbed   bought   cheered

1 Dad _____ a new lawnmower.
2 We _____ when Darren scored a goal.
3 Nicola _____ so softly I could not hear her.
4 The cat _____ up the tall tree.
5 My mother _____ a cake for our School Fair.

Writing sentences

Add words of your own to make good sentences.
The pictures will help you.

1 The farmer

2 Pam buys

3 The elephant

4 The astronaut

5 The painter

6 The ship

7 Susan

8 The train

9 The monkeys

10 The boys

Mixed bag

A Write out the two words meaning the same.
For example: **halt** run **stop** hop

1 fall	lift	drop	push
2 start	begin	end	carry
3 huge	little	small	circle
4 ocean	beach	cliff	sea
5 fast	slow	quick	stop

B Write out these words in order of size.
Begin with the largest.
For example:
cat   elephant   mouse   →   **elephant   cat   mouse**

1 page	word	book
2 tree	branch	leaf
3 ten	six	one
4 week	year	day
5 frog	giraffe	dog

C Which is always wet?
For example: brush **rain** bucket spade

1 cakes	pies	lemonade	bread
2 grass	trees	flowers	pond
3 lake	hill	mountain	path
4 bridge	river	lane	road
5 cliffs	sand	rock	sea

Mixed bag

A Make a new word using the same letters.

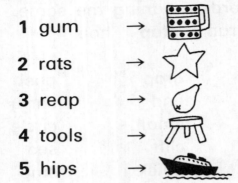

1 gum →
2 rats →
3 reap →
4 tools →
5 hips →

B Write out the opposite of these words.
Choose from this list.

| sell   empty   dirty   last   soft   odd   awake   shut |

1 even _____
2 clean _____
3 buy _____
4 open _____

5 hard _____
6 asleep _____
7 full _____
8 first _____

C Write out the correct answer.

1 Which is not a flower?   (snowdrop, rose, buttercup, lettuce)
2 Which is not a fish?   (salmon, duck, pike, herring)
3 Which is not a bird?   (thrush, robin, fly, gull)
4 Which is not a tree?   (ash, pine, oak, grass)
5 Which is not a colour?   (yellow, down, green, red)
6 Which is not a fruit?   (apple, pair, orange, banana)
7 Which is not a food?   (bread, biscuit, plate, cake)
8 Which is not a boy's name?   (David, Derek, Jane, Edwin)

Answers

Page 2 Name these things

1 ant 2 axe 3 apple 4 acrobat 5 anchor 6 bat
7 bus 8 bee 9 ball 10 bed 11 cat 12 cap 13 car
14 cup 15 camel

Page 3 Name these things

1 dog 2 duck 3 desk 4 egg 5 elephant 6 fox
7 fish 8 fire 9 girl 10 garden 11 hen 12 hat
13 hand 14 horse 15 hammer

Page 4 Name these things

1 insect 2 jelly 3 jam 4 key 5 king 6 kite 7 lion
8 lemon 9 ladder 10 lamb 11 milk 12 mat
13 moon 14 nose 15 nest

Page 5 Name these things

1 orange 2 octopus 3 pin 4 pig 5 pipe 6 queen
7 rat 8 ruler 9 robin 10 roof 11 sun 12 saw
13 tap 14 tent 15 tree

Page 6 Name these things

1 table 2 tiger 3 umbrella 4 van 5 vase 6 witch
7 windmill 8 window 9 watch 10 wall 11 yak
12 yacht 13 zip 14 zebra 15 zoo

Page 7 First sounds

1 ball 2 dart 3 pan 4 bed 5 domino 6 penny
7 book 8 doll

Page 8 Seen at the seaside
1 pier 2 sandcastle 3 yacht 4 cliffs 5 spade
6 seaweed 7 crab 8 rocks 9 deckchair 10 seagull
11 speedboat 12 fish 13 pebbles 14 net

Page 9 Sorting animals
1 camel 2 dog 3 cow 4 rabbit 5 giraffe 6 cat
7 sheep 8 hen 9 pig 10 gorilla 11 leopard
12 hamster
home dog, cat, rabbit, hamster
farm cow, hen, sheep, pig
zoo camel, giraffe, gorilla, leopard

Page 10 Watch us
1 skip 2 climb 3 jump 4 slide 5 run 6 swim

Page 11 More than one (1)
1 ladders 2 balls 3 houses 4 birds 5 cars
6 books 7 stars 8 flowers

Page 12 At home
1 chair 2 television 3 carpet 4 picture 5 vase
6 books 7 settee 8 lamp 9 curtains 10 window
11 table 12 door 13 radio 14 fire

Page 13 Young animals
1 kitten 2 puppy 3 chicken 4 duckling 5 calf
6 foal 7 lamb 8 piglet

Page 14 Ball play
1 head **2** throw **3** roll **4** kick **5** catch **6** bounce

Page 15 Crosswords
1 bat, ball **2** fox, fish **3** car, cow **4** axe, apple
5 dog, duck **6** box, boat **7** hammer, hen
8 kite, key **9** table, tap **10** sack, saw

Page 16 More than one (2)
1 matches **2** glasses **3** boxes **4** churches **5** trees
6 foxes **7** buses **8** dishes

Page 17 At school
1 balance **2** milk **3** paints **4** aquarium **5** books
6 brushes **7** sand-tray **8** scissors **9** oven **10** ruler
11 work-tray **12** pencils **13** sink **14** easel

Page 18 Animal homes
1 sett **2** kennel **3** hive **4** stable **5** burrow **6** sty
7 den **8** nest

Page 19 They are busy
1 sew **2** paint **3** fish **4** bake **5** sing **6** dig

Page 20 a in the middle
1 pan **2** jam **3** cap **4** mat **5** bag

e in the middle
1 hen **2** bed **3** ten **4** leg **5** pen

Page 21 i in the middle
1 lip 2 bin 3 pin 4 tin 5 pig

o in the middle
1 cot 2 mop 3 log 4 dog 5 rod

Page 22 u in the middle
1 rug 2 bull 3 sun 4 mug 5 bus

Mixed bag
1 cat 2 nut 3 pod 4 web 5 bin

Page 23 In the park
1 John 2 three 3 Andy 4 Susan 5 Rod, Mark 6 Sally
7 Cathy, Andrew 8 seven 9 Jill, Gary 10 ten

Page 24 Word puzzle (1)
1 bee 2 car 3 saw 4 boy 5 cow 6 bat 7 bed 8 dog 9 cat
10 sun 11 mug 12 bus 13 tap 14 web

Page 25 Animal sounds
1 purrs 2 barks 3 grunts 4 quacks 5 roars 6 bleats
7 chatters 8 hoots

Page 26 oo in the middle
1 book 2 hook 3 boot 4 pool 5 goose 6 rook 7 root 8 roof
9 stool 10 broom 11 hoop 12 brook

Page 27 Rhymes (1)
1 can 2 tap 3 cat 4 red 5 ten 6 pet 7 rib 8 kid 9 wig
10 dip 11 fin 12 pod 13 dog 14 top 15 dot 16 mud 17
mug 18 gun 19 pup 20 nut

Page 28 Choose the right word
1 plaice **2** ant **3** buoy **4** bear **5** beach **6** key **7** pail **8** sea
9 rose **10** flower **11** wood **12** pear

Page 29 Double letters
1 apple **2** cheese **3** ladder **4** cabbage **5** arrow **6** button
7 jelly **8** food

Page 30 People at work
1 dentist **2** fireman **3** nurse **4** pilot **5** butcher **6** vet **7** baker
8 postman

Page 31 Word puzzles (2)
1 boat **2** bird **3** fish **4** girl **5** leaf **6** moon **7** foot **8** loaf
9 book **10** tree **11** goat **12** duck **13** nail **14** king

Page 32 Crosswords
1 flag, flower **2** claw, clown **3** drum, dress **4** shell, ship
5 spoon, spade **6** church, chair **7** three, thumb **8** star, step
9 swan, swing

Page 33 Completing sentences
A 1 The gorilla was in the zoo. **2** Birds have feathers.
3 The fish swam away. **4** The airliner landed at the airport.
5 Mark scored a goal. **6** A house has a roof.
B 1 shuts **2** wags **3** milks **4** looks **5** brings **6** drives **7** rides
8 washes **9** brushes **10** sleeps

Page 34 What are they?
1 fruits **2** seasons **3** birds **4** numbers **5** fish **6** months
7 letters **8** tools **9** boys **10** flowers

Page 35 Words that begin with ch
1 chips **2** chalk **3** church **4** child **5** chest **6** chair

Words that end with ch
1 torch **2** pitch **3** March **4** watch **5** witch **6** match

Page 36 Colours
1 yellow **2** white **3** green **4** brown **5** black **6** silver **7** red
8 blue

Opposites
1 new **2** early **3** fast **4** weak **5** hard **6** wet **7** quiet **8** empty
9 dirty **10** straight

Page 37 Rhymes (2)
1 cry **2** head **3** train **4** day **5** nail **6** meat **7** moon **8** blow
9 toy **10** now **11** rose **12** blue **13** hate **14** sold **15** sun
16 fair **17** lane **18** maid **19** bird **20** there

Page 38 is or are
1 is **2** are **3** is **4** is **5** are **6** Is **7** are **8** is **9** Are **10** are

was or were
1 was **2** was **3** were **4** was **5** were **6** Was **7** were **8** were
9 were **10** Were

Page 39 Who's who?
1 miner **2** farmer **3** nurse **4** vet **5** fisherman **6** dentist
7 pilot **8** fireman

Page 40 Jumbled sentences

1 Mark scored a goal. **2** Ian cut his finger. **3** The cat licks her paw. **4** Kate fell into the pond. **5** Dad cuts the lawn. **6** Heather lit the bonfire. **7** Andrew posted a letter. **8** The horse jumped over the gate.

Page 41 a and an

1 a **2** an **3** a **4** a **5** an **6** an **7** a **8** a **9** an **10** a **11** an **12** an **13** a **14** a **15** an

1 an **2** an **3** an **4** an **5** an **6** a **7** an, a **8** a, an **9** an, a **10** an, an

Page 42 By the seaside

1 four **2** David, Rod **3** Mark, Paul **4** Carol, Heather **5** Andrew, Clare **6** starfish **7** Mrs Rigby, Mrs Conroy **8** DC 452

Page 43 Choosing words

A eggs, bread, apples, bacon, onions, cakes
B fields, plough, barn, cows, hens, tractor
C boots, jackets, shoes, jeans, shirts, skirts
D buses, bicycles, motorbikes, taxis, lorries, cars

Page 44 Find the best word

A 1 cruel **2** blind **3** brave **4** heavy **5** busy
B 1 steep **2** sweet **3** sharp **4** loud **5** sour
C 1 fierce **2** unhappy **3** bright **4** dirty **5** difficult

Page 45 The best word

A 1 ate **2** swam **3** banged **4** asked **5** blew
B 1 marched **2** drank **3** flew **4** chased **5** crawled
C 1 bought **2** cheered **3** whispered **4** climbed **5** baked

Page 46 Writing sentences

1 – 10 Check that your child's sentences describe the matching pictures.

Page 47 Mixed bag

A 1 fall, drop **2** start, begin **3** little, small
4 ocean, sea **5** fast, quick
B 1 book, page, word **2** tree, branch, leaf **3** ten, six, one **4** year, week, day **5** giraffe, dog, frog
C 1 lemonade **2** pond **3** lake **4** river **5** sea

Page 48 Mixed bag

A 1 mug **2** star **3** pear **4** stool **5** ship
B 1 odd **2** dirty **3** sell **4** shut **5** soft **6** awake
7 empty **8** last
C 1 lettuce **2** duck **3** fly **4** grass **5** down **6** pair
7 plate **8** Jane